The Day

Nothing

Happened

THE DAY NOTHING HAPPENED

The hour

by hour

story

of the

most

uneventful

Thursday

in American

history

by

COREY FORD

Doubleday & Company, Inc., Garden City, New York   *1959*

Library of Congress Catalog Card Number 59–12681
Copyright © 1959 by Corey Ford
Copyright © 1959 by The Curtis Publishing Company
All Rights Reserved
Printed in the United States of America
Designed by Diana Klemin
First Edition

CONTENTS

CONTENTS

ILLUSTRATIONS

following page twenty-four

Christmas card from the Hostetters. *From the author's collection.*
ROSS PHOTOS

Tracks of New York Central. BETTMAN ARCHIVE

LeRoy Goss's appointment calendar. *From the author's collection.*
ROSS PHOTOS

Main Street of Bronxville, N.Y.

Mrs. Heppner's dental diagram. *From the author's collection.*
ROSS PHOTOS

Neighborhood bar on lower Fourth Avenue. WIDE WORLD PHOTOS

Unmarked door (locked) on sixth floor. ROSS PHOTOS

Sign at 23rd Street and Fourth Avenue. ROSS PHOTOS

Illustrations

Advertisement of Thursday sale at S. Klein. *From the author's collection.* ROSS PHOTOS

Paper-wrapped parcel. ROSS PHOTOS

Paris, France, at 10 P.M. on Thursday. PHOTO JOHN CRAVEN

Tracks of New York Central. BETTMAN ARCHIVE

Aerial view of Scranton, Pennsylvania. PHOTO ROTKIN, P.F.I.

facing page fifty-eight

Thursday's survivors. *From the author's collection.* ROSS PHOTOS

FOR THE RECORD

This book represents nineteen years of solid work. (Twenty, if you count the year it will take me to get my desk straightened up again.) There were endless statistics to be gathered, and newspaper items to be cut out and indexed and filed, and old handbills to be pored over, and eyewitness accounts of survivors to be pieced together. The outlay in paper clips alone was astronomical.

But of course that's the whole secret of a book like this: research. You pick a day when some historic disaster took place, and set down everything that happened in the course of twenty-four hours. The more details you pile up, the more suspense you build. Just keep mentioning the time (to the exact minute) and work in an ominous phrase now and then, such as "Little did he know as he left the White House this night that he would never return" or "None of the passengers in that glittering saloon on A-deck would live to see the dawn." You don't even need a plot.

My hardest job was finding a day that hadn't been used already. They've been turning out these stop-watch epics so fast that there aren't many open dates left. I thought of the Day that Lincoln Was Shot, but Jim Bishop had tackled that. John Hersey had covered Hiroshima, and Walter Lord had handled Pearl Harbor. Somebody had taken D-Day, I found, and somebody else had done the *Andrea Doria*. The Civil War was pretty well spoken for, from the Firing on Fort Sumter to the Surrender at Appomattox, and the *Titanic* had sunk so often lately that it was becoming waterlogged. I finally decided on Thursday of this week, because none of the other writers had gotten around to it yet. What's more, Thursday was completely indistinguishable from any other day, so if someone else grabs it before I finish my book, I can still change it to Wednesday or even Tuesday.

As a student of Thursday, I kept a careful record of all the events that happened from morning to night, labeling my notebooks 7 A.M., 8 A.M., 9 A.M., and so on. In addition, I kept a notebook entitled "Yesterday" and another called "Tomorrow," because you never know. Despite my efforts, certain small errors were detected in the galleys by other Thursday scholars. Thus, for example, I had assumed that the man called Nick Zykwscx had to cross Fifth Avenue to get to Broadway, whereas several people who were actually in New York on Thursday pointed out that Broadway runs east of Fifth Avenue below 23rd Street. To make doubly sure of my facts, therefore, I personally retraced the route of the assassin from East 12th Street to the Bon Ton store and north to 25th Street and Fourth Avenue, stopping at each of the small bars he had visited, in company with a member of the State Alcoholic Beverage Commission, a Mr. Reeper or Deeper. As a result of this investigation, I did not get back to work until two days later, and Mr. Neeper has not been heard from yet. I mention this merely to indicate the extensive research that goes into a book like this.

For help in amassing my material, I should like to express my thanks to Mr. Leeper; Mr. F. L. Peters of the Information Booth at Grand Central Station, who supplied me with timetables of both the New Haven Railroad and the New York Central (Harlem Division); the 1958–59 Manhattan Telephone Directory; the Rand-McNally Company, who let me see an old map of New York showing the location of Fourth Avenue; a Mr. and Mrs. Frank Hostetter of Toledo,

For the Record

Ohio, who sent me a card last Christmas; and the authors
of all the other Day Books, but for whose efforts this one
might never have been written.

Corey Ford

THE
MORNING
HOURS

7:00   a.m.

8:00   a.m.

9:00   a.m.

10:00   a.m.

11:00   a.m.

7:00 a.m.

On Thursday morning the 7:58 New York local pulled into Bronxville at 8:07.

A wan sun pinkened the clouds of the new dawn. Suburban Bronxville was coming alive, and commuters swarmed the long cement platform to board the train for Manhattan City, many carrying newspapers under their arms. Headlines of the day spoke of satellites and the national budget, and in the *Herald Tribune* Joseph Alsop warned of another Near East crisis. In the smoking car Mr. B. A. Johansen, a resident of Scarsdale, turned to ask his seat companion, Mr. Harry

Creevey of Hartsdale, whether they were running a little slow, and Mr. Creevey replied, according to Mr. Johansen, that he "thought so." A more exact recollection is that of the conductor, Mr. Leland Harcourt, who remembers distinctly looking at his timepiece, a Hamilton, and remarking: "We're eleven minutes behind." This would seem to establish the time of departure as 8:09.

As the train pulled out, a stout bespectacled figure wearing the expression of one who is late was seen running down the platform, carrying a rectangular brief case and waving a folded umbrella. It was Mr. LeRoy Goss of 121 Maple Avenue, Bronxville. He had missed it again.

At this same moment, several miles away, a dapper side-burned man named Ansel Blodgett, employed as a window dresser at S. Klein's department store on Union Square in New York, was boarding the 8:10 local at Columbus Avenue in Mount Vernon. Ansel Blodgett had never met LeRoy Goss, but their paths were destined to cross less than four hours hence.

LeRoy Goss had overslept this morning. His wife, Mrs. Goss, had called upstairs to him several times, but his wrist watch was being repaired, so Mr. Goss did not awaken until 7:31. He shaved hurriedly, nicking himself on the cheek about an inch below the left ear, and unnoticed in his haste he left the hot-water tap running, a small but steady trickle. He was to be reminded forcibly of this later. While he was eating breakfast, a poached egg on toast, Mrs. Goss mentioned that she would drive him to the station because she needed the car to keep her Friday appointment with the hairdresser, Dolores. Mr. Goss pointed out that today was only Thursday.

"I thought it was Friday," Mrs. Goss said.

She was never to keep her appointment.

8:00 a.m.

Thursday in Manhattan City began like any other. The streets, even at this hour, were filled with people going to work. New York was a metropolis of many persons with diverse passions and ambitions. Some in the city would be born today and others would die. These were the unknowns, the unremembereds. Small pebbles in small pools.

As LeRoy Goss emerged from the lower level of Grand Central Station, being without his watch, he observed that the hands of the clock above the Information Booth stood at 8:47, and so he elected to save time by taking the subway to 23rd Street and Fourth Avenue. Had he traveled by bus, as was his wont, he might have seen J. Frankel, proprietor of a small pet shop on the corner of 26th Street, in the act of feeding some tropical parakeets in his show window.

Thus does history hang by a slender thread.

At this same moment, in a rear room of a disorderly house on 12th Street just east of Fourth Avenue, a man named Nick Zykwscx sat on the edge of his bed, hungover and bloodshot of eye. Three years ago he had changed his name to Nick Kyzwscx, but it wasn't any better that way so he had changed it back. He was small and unshaven-faced, with the expression of one who does not like what he must do this day. He pulled on his pants silently, carrying his shoes to the door lest he waken the blonde in bed, also disorderly. His hand shook a little, and on his way out he paused to take a drink from the bottle on the dresser, in order to fortify himself for that which lay ahead.

Despondently Nick Zykwscx shuffled down the creaking staircase to the street, a helpless tool of destiny.

9:00 a.m.

Mr. Goss's office was located at 24th Street and Fourth
Avenue on the sixth floor of a brownstone-fronted building
that had seen better days, but not much better. The edifice
was 64 feet wide by 123 feet deep and rose to a height of
ten stories, the upper two vacant. Many of the building's
tenants were engaged in the import trade, as indeed was the
firm for which Mr. Goss worked, it importing ostrich
plumes. Adjoining his office was a firm called "Manhattan
Derrick and Steamshovel Co., Inc.," of which little can be
learned, and at the far end of the corridor was an unmarked

door which was always locked. By one of the great ironies of history, though Mr. Goss could not see it from his office window, the building was only a stone's throw from the site where Madison Square Garden no longer stood in which, on June 25, 1906, Harry K. Thaw was to shoot Stanford White in an affair of the heart. Thus does passion spiral to insanity.

The elevator being out of order, it was necessary for Mr. Goss to walk bent-legged up six flights of stairs. His secretary, Mrs. Freda Heppner, had been with him for eleven years, but on this Thursday she was suffering from an infected upper right molar (though later she was to claim it was an upper left molar)* and so it was that her place had been taken by a Miss Loretta Runkel, a large blonde from Biloxi, Mississippi, wearing the expression of one who is asleep. As Mr. Goss entered the office he said, "Good morning, Mrs. Heppner," and Miss Runkel, according to at least one witness, an office boy named Jerry, replied, "I'm Miss Runkel," or, more accurately, "Ah'm Miss Runkel." Mr. Goss asked if there was any mail, and Mrs. Heppner or, more accurately, Miss Runkel said no. He then sat down at his desk and crossed his legs, his right foot flexing up and down pensively. Business was slack, the Metropolitan Opera season not being open.

---

*Her dentist, Dr. H. Fried, insists it was the right molar, and offers the extracted denture in proof.

Christmas card received
from Mr. and Mrs. Frank
Hostetter of Toledo, Ohio.
*From the author's
collection.*

Tracks of New York Central (looking south) two minutes before
arrival of 7:58 New York local on which LeRoy Goss was not riding.

Neighborhood bar on lower Fourth Avenue which Nick Zykwscx did not visit, it having been torn down in 1907.

Main Street of Bronxville, N. Y. Arrow indicates approximate location of hairdressing establishment where Mrs. Goss was not to keep her Friday appointment.

Dental diagram by Dr. H. Fried. Arrow indicates approximate location of upper right molar extracted from Mrs. Heppner. *From the author's collection.*

Name   Heppner, Mrs. F.

Thurs. *Date*   November 5   19⁵⁹

Remarks _____ Remove upper right molar.

                    H. Fried, D.D.

Appointment calendar from desk of LeRoy Goss, showing his efforts to recall that which he had forgotten this day. *From the author's collection.*

THURSDAY, NOVEMBER 5, 1959

Paris, France, at 10 p.m. on Thursday, which would be 5 p.m. in Manhattan City. (NOTE: This picture was taken at 10 a.m.)

Tracks of New York Central (looking north) two minutes after departure of 5:13 White Plains local which Mr. Goss also missed.

Advertisement of Thursday sale at S. Klein's department store on Union Square. *From the author's collection.*

S. KLEIN

Fashion Annex

NEW YORK · HEMPSTEAD

ON SALE THURSDAY 10 A.M.

MISSES! JUNIORS!
GET ALL THE
FASHION-NEWS IN

SUMMER
DRESSES

all FAR below original wholesale!
many below the cost to make!

$8 $11
and

SEE THESE FABRICS: A CLUE TO THE

MR. LeRoy Goss

Paper-wrapped parcel
similar in appearance to
that carried by the man
called Zykwscx.

Unmarked door (locked) on sixth floor of office building wherein LeRoy Goss was employed.

Sign at intersection of 23rd Street and Fourth Avenue. (NOTE: The latter name was changed to Park Avenue South after this book was published.)

Aerial view of Scranton, Pennsylvania. Nothing happened in Scranton on Thursday, either.

Ten blocks to the south, in a window of S. Klein's facing Union Square, Ansel Blodgett, his street shoes encased in felt slippers, was dressing mannikins with flowered straw hats, a popular style of the era. Ansel Blodgett had arrived at work earlier than Mr. Goss, having caught the express to 14th Street. He decorated with haste, for the time was 9:56, and in four minutes the doors of S. Klein's would open to admit the throng of shoppers without. Already they lined the sidewalk in front of the window, their noses pressed to the pane like goldfish in an aquarium, perhaps in Frankel's pet shop.

Ansel Blodgett affixed a daisy-festooned straw to the head of a wax model, and his glance encountered a craven figure, unshaven of jowl, moving not too steadily through the crowd. For a moment their eyes met, but neither gave a sign of recognition. Nick Zykwscx zigzagged across Union Square to the other side of the park and entered a small bar on Broadway to fortify himself for his unpleasant assignment.

Even as he did so, the doors of S. Klein's swung open. Thursday's work had begun.

Others good and bad were busy at work on this fateful morning. In the shadowy interior of a store called "Bon Ton," on Broadway at the northwest corner of 16th Street, a solitary individual was bent over a table, clad in shirt sleeves and a vest only. He was in his early forties, with lean feminine features which could be cruel, and his pointed black mustache was freshly pomaded. Later many would say that he was the scion of a wealthy family who had left home after a bitter altercation. His delicate tapering fingers plied themselves expertly to his sinister task, assembling screws and bolts and pieces of wire to complete the object on the table before him. A large knife, unsheathed, lay at his elbow, and smoke curled from a cigarette between his thin lips, drawn back in a confident smile. He knew for whom this object was intended.

Inexorably the course of events was moving to its climax.

10:00 a.m.

A convalescent sun, weak and pale, blinked through the mist over Manhattan City. LeRoy Goss, seated at his desk, uncrossed his legs and crossed them the other way, his left foot flexing pensively. His wife, Mrs. Goss, had given him a list of things to purchase in town today, but he had misplaced it. He knew she wanted a spool of silk thread to match the sample in his pocket, but there was something else she had told him to be sure and not forget. For an hour he had been sitting here, trying to recall what it was. Several times he had thought of calling up Mrs. Goss in Bronxville to ask her, and once his hand actually strayed to the phone, but he recalled it. Instead he asked Mrs. Heppner or, rather, Miss Runkel what time it was.

"10:39," replied Miss Runkel.

Miss Runkel was wrong. The time, according to the electric clock on the wall of the Bon Ton store on Broadway, was 10:40. At a table in the rear the pomade-mustached man worked intently to wrap the object he had completed in brown paper. He knotted the string with tapering fingers as a craven figure staggered into the store.

"You are late," he said, his lip curling in ill-concealed disgust at his hireling's fetid breath. "This must reach its destination ere five."

With a flourish he uncapped his fountain pen, wrote on the parcel a name, and drew a map showing the location at 24th Street and Fourth Avenue. He placed the object in Zykwscx's shaking hands.

"Make sure it is presented in person," he instructed in a tone that did not brook refusal. "There can be no mistake."

Zykwscx's face was pale, and his tongue darted to moisten his dry lips. Holding the parcel to his ear, he could detect an unmistakable ticking sound. Dully he focused his eyes to read the name the other had written.

It was LeRoy Goss.

Reluctantly the man called Nick Zykwscx shuffled out of the store and headed for a small bar across the street to fortify himself some more for the task he must perform before the day was done. To the west, many farmers testified that, at this moment, the sun emerged full from clouds blood-red.

11:00 a.m.

LeRoy Goss was worried. Still he could not remember that which his wife had told him not to forget. He had a feeling it started with *p,* but he had run through all the possibilities in his mind: pomegranates, parcheesi, pumpkin pie, ping-pong balls. At 11:31, having ascertained the time from Miss Runkel, he picked up the telephone and called his house in Bronxville. Then he made a startling discovery.

Mrs. Goss was not there.

After Eva Goss had dropped her husband off at the station, acting on a sudden impulse, she had decided not to wait until the following day to have her hair done by Dolores, and so she had driven to a beauty parlor in White Plains. She was a woman of great determination, and when she was born she was to marry LeRoy Goss twenty-three years later. Her hair-do accomplished, and it being then 11:09, she had called at the house of a friend, Mrs. Elsie Creevey of Hartsdale, a relative by marriage of the Harry Creevey who had taken the train to New York earlier this morning, and asked if she was ready to attend the regular Friday Bridge Club luncheon at the Westchester Country Club. Mrs. Creevey had pointed out that Friday was tomorrow.

"I've been mixed up all day," is Mrs. Creevey's version of what Mrs. Goss replied.

Eva Goss then drove back to her home at 121 Maple Avenue, a modest suburban dwelling. The phone was ringing as she opened the door, but when she picked it up the operator said the other party had hung up.

Thus does fate flip a silver coin to fall which way it will.

At 11:32, having tried without success to reach his wife, LeRoy Goss elected to leave the office early, intending to purchase the spool of silk thread during his lunch hour. He could not yet recall what else she had told him to get, but he thought he'd better buy the thread before he forgot that, too. There is no record that his secretary warned him: "You should not go to S. Klein's this day." Unsuspecting, Mr. Goss walked bent-legged down the six flights to the street, the elevator still not running. He headed south on Fourth Avenue, keeping to the right-hand side of that thoroughfare, and crossed to the left-hand side at 20th Street. Had he continued on the right-hand side for another block, and had he glanced in the window of a small bar at 19th Street, and had he seen Nick Zykwscx there, and had he known him even if he had, the outcome of Thursday's history might have been altered.

The man called Zykwscx had been making erratic but steady progress north, pausing at each small bar for further fortification. Now there were no more bars between 19th and 24th streets. The moment was at hand.

Mr. Goss, still unsuspecting, proceeded on his way downtown, holding to the left-hand side of Fourth Avenue. As he approached S. Klein's on Union Square, a dapper sideburned man came out of the store and passed in front of him. Ansel Blodgett had crossed his path.

The time was 11:44.

At 11:59, having applied lipstick and adjusted her girdle, Loretta Runkel prepared to depart the sixth-floor office. As

33

she opened the door, she found herself face to face with a craven figure standing in the hall, holding a brown paper parcel. Later in her testimony Miss Runkel was to maintain that she heard it ticking. The man, teetering slightly, asked in a thick voice: "Is Mister Goss inside?"

"He's gone to lunch," Miss Runkel claims she replied, though it is more probable that what she said was: "He-all's gone to lunch."

"I'll be back," the man said.

The stone had been dropped in the still pool. Now the waves began to ripple outward in ever-widening circles.

THE
AFTERNOON
HOURS

12   noon

1:00   p.m.

2:00   p.m.

3:00   p.m.

4:00   p.m.

5:00   p.m.

12 noon

At noon in Manhattan City the streets were filled with people. Some walked fast and some walked slow, bound for their midday repast. In the pet shop on 26th Street, J. Frankel told his assistant to tend the parakeets while he was out. Seven years hence he was to sell his store and move to California. On the other side of town Mr. Harry Creevey met Mr. B. A. Johansen, as was their custom, and they walked to lunch together, arguing amiably. "Today is on me," Mr. Creevey insisted, and Mr. Johansen replied, "No,

this is mine," and Mr. Creevey answered, "You had yesterday," and Mr. Johansen agreed, "All right, I'll take tomorrow." Against a bar on 25th Street, opposite Mr. Goss's office,
the man called Nick Zykwscx leaned bent-elbowed, fortifying
himself yet more for that which must be done.

On adjoining stools at a counter in the Pennsylvania
Drug Store, on the corner of Fourth Avenue and 23rd Street,
Ansel Blodgett sat in whispered conversation with Loretta
Runkel.* Many have denied that their meeting was acci-
dental, but there is no shred of evidence to support the
accusation that the rendezvous was prearranged. According
to Miss Runkel's story, she just happened to sit down on
the stool, it being the only one vacant, and while she was
having a chocolate frappe and a piece of fudge cake, her
regular lunch, this total stranger she had never set eyes on
before just happened to get talking to her. The stranger
asked her if she was doing anything after work tonight, and
Miss Runkel told him that she didn't know for sure, she'd
have to think it over, whereupon the stranger, leaning closer,
asked if he could call her at the office later this afternoon.
Miss Runkel then wrote down the number with lipstick on
a piece of Kleenex.

Thus it was that Ansel Blodgett came into possession of
LeRoy Goss's phone number.

---

*Some historians claim this encounter took place outdoors on horseback.

Twenty miles north, in the suburban dwelling at 121 Maple Avenue, Mrs. Eva Goss was sitting down at this same moment to a luncheon of cottage cheese and lettuce she had prepared for herself, being on a diet. The first mouthful was barely between her lips when she heard a short imperative knock at the kitchen door. A heavy-set man in overalls was standing on the step, carrying a square black bag. Mrs. Goss, swallowing, asked him what he wanted, and the man replied with a foreign accent: "I come to fix ya washing machine."

"I thought you were supposed to come on Thursday," Mrs. Goss said irritably.

"This is Thursday," the man replied.

"I keep thinking it's Friday," was Mrs. Goss's reply.

1:00 p.m.

The noon hour was over, and the streets of Manhattan City were filled with people walking back from their midday repast. J. Frankel, returning to his pet shop on 26th Street, passed the man called Nick Zykwscx as he lurched out of the bar on 25th Street and lurched into another bar on 24th Street. Nick Zykwscx, glancing through the window, caught the eye of Ansel Blodgett as he escorted Miss Runkel to her office, but there was no sign of recognition. Ansel Blodgett, starting back downtown on the left-hand side of Fourth Avenue, passed LeRoy Goss as he hurried back uptown on the right-hand side of Fourth Avenue, bound for his appointment with destiny.

Patrolman Timothy O'Rourke, directing the traffic at the 23rd Street intersection, shook his head. "How will all this end?" he mused aloud.

Now a silence settled over the great metropolis as people sank back in swivel chairs after lunch, eyes closed. The unnatural quiet was broken only by the sound of heavy breathing and occasionally a deep abdominal rumble. For the next hour in the city nothing whatsoever happened.

2:00 p.m.

3:00 p.m.

Only LeRoy Goss, having missed his lunch this day because he was shopping, had not been sleeping. He sat at his desk, flexing first his left leg and then his right, lost in thought. Still his mind sought to remember that which Mrs. Goss had told him, but to no avail. Time was running out its course.

At 3:17 he rose deliberately from his desk. Watching him, one might have guessed that he knew what he had to do. He put his fragile spectacles in a case, removed his coat, and hung it on the rack. Self-consciously he walked past Miss

Runkel to the door, his lips pulled back in a forced half-smile. With lowered head he strode down the corridor past the adjoining office of the Manhattan Derrick and Steamshovel Co., Inc., turned a corner, and halted before the unmarked door at the far end of the hall. He took a key from his pocket, turned it in the lock, and entered.

Even as the door clicked shut behind him, a small figure dragged himself heavily up the stairs and staggered toward Mr. Goss's office. He supported himself in the doorway, with one hand on the frame, and his bloodshot eyes swept the room. In his hand was the brown paper parcel, still ticking.

" 'S Mist'r Goss here?" he asked in slurred tones.

"He just stepped out," said Miss Runkel.

" 'll be back," Nick Zykwscx muttered, and stumbled back down the stairs, just as the unmarked door at the end of the hall opened and LeRoy Goss emerged with the look of one who has done what he must. He strolled along the corridor to his office, washed his hands at a small basin in the corner, and put his coat back on. He sat down at his desk, crossing his legs again.

Sometimes on such a tiny hinge does the gate of history swing.

4:00 p.m.

Eva Goss was a woman given to uncanny intuitions. It was her contention, oft expressed to Mr. Goss, that the female of the species had an occult sixth sense which a mere male did not possess. Some of her intimations of disaster bordered on the supernatural, as witness the occasion, some years ago, when she had urged Mr. Goss to turn back to the house as they were setting out for a drive, because she had a premonition she left her cigarette burning somewhere. Mr. Goss could not find her cigarette, but while he was looking for it he had laid his lighted cigar on the hall table, and

47

the house had burned to the ground. Mrs. Goss could not have been more pleased.

And so it was that on this Thursday afternoon, awakening from a fitful slumber, Eva Goss had a sudden hunch to telephone her husband. It cannot be stated with accuracy that she suspected he had forgotten what she told him to purchase in the city, but the fact remains, according to the sworn statement of the Bronxville long-distance operator on duty that day, a Miss Bluebell Durgin, that Mrs. Goss actually placed a call to the office in New York at 4:23. She was told by the operator that the line was busy, and so after waiting a long time she hung up.

Mrs. Goss could not know that it was Loretta Runkel on the phone, talking to Ansel Blodgett.

At 4:29 Miss Runkel, hanging up the phone, had pleaded a sick headache and asked if it would be all right to leave the office a little early. Mr. Goss giving his assent, she had departed in great haste, he saying to her, "Good night, Mrs. Heppner," and she replying over her shoulder, "Ah'm Miss Runkel." Now LeRoy Goss was alone. He had no idea what time it was, not being able to ask Miss Runkel, but in his heart he must have been aware that this day was nearing its predestined end.

Already a setting sun incarnadined the office buildings of Manhattan City, and in the distance the chimes of the Metropolitan Tower boomed five times.

5:00 p.m.

No one asked what the bells meant, or, if he did, it is not recorded that he did. In a trice, the metropolis resembled a hive immediately after the queen bee has died. The streets were jammed with people going home from work. At the same moment, in Paris, France, people were setting out for the Montmartre after a late supper, while in California, where J. Frankel was to live after he sold his pet shop, people were just getting back from lunch. Somewhere in the Pacific a great ocean liner sailed across the International Date Line, and a steward told the passengers solemnly: "Today is tomorrow now." On the other side of the world, Thursday was already over.

LeRoy Goss, reaching for his brief case and umbrella, heard the office door open behind him. He turned to confront a craven figure swaying in the entranceway, a brown paper parcel in his hand. There was no panic, no sign of fear, no effort to run. LeRoy Goss had the expression of one who knows his time has come. The man's voice was almost inaudible: "Mis'r Moss?"

"Goss," LeRoy Goss corrected with quiet dignity.

"I'm fr'm Bon Ton," the man called Nick Zykwscx said, holding out the ticking object. "'S two doll'rs c'lect."

Mr. Goss paid the money, and took his wrist watch out of the parcel. The hands stood at 5:08. With a stifled groan, he galloped bent-legged down the six flights of stairs, the elevator not yet running, and sprinted along Fourth Avenue toward the subway. Following him downstairs, though more slowly, Nick Zykwscx staggered across the street into the bar on 24th Street and laid the two bills on the counter. *

---

*Perhaps, like me, you wonder what will happen to some of the people who played a key role in this day of destiny. Nick Zykwscx, having spent the $2.00 on drink, will be dismissed from the employ of Bon Ton the following morn. Later he will change his name back to Kyzwscx and wind up his days in the disorderly house on East 12th Street. Loretta Runkel will not marry

Mr. Harry Creevey met Mr. B. A. Johansen at the Information Booth on the lower level of Grand Central Station, and together they walked through a gate marked "5:13 White Plains Local." As the bars slammed shut behind them, a short bespectacled figure was seen running across the terminal, carrying an umbrella and waving a brief case.

LeRoy Goss had missed the train again.

Ansel Blodgett, he being the father of two children in Mount Vernon. Patrolman O'Rourke, at his request, will be transferred to Houston Street.

The elevator in Mr. Goss's building will not be running tomorrow either.

THE EVENING HOURS

6:00 p.m.

6:00 p.m.

Eva Goss was waiting in the car at the Bronxville station when Mr. Goss arrived at 6:03. Her first words were: "Did you remember to get the parakeet food like I asked you?"

"That's what I was trying to think of all day," Mr. Goss said. "I knew there was something I'd forgotten."

"You forgot and left the hot-water tap running this morning, too," Mrs. Goss reminded him forcibly.

In the modest suburban dwelling at 121 Maple Avenue they sat down to a supper of creamed halibut, which Mrs. Goss had ordered under the impression it was Friday. Mr.

Goss ate in silence, and Mrs. Goss, wearing the expression of someone who is trying to make conversation, asked: "What happened in the city today?"

"Nothing," said Mr. Goss, removing a halibut bone from his mouth and placing it on his butter plate.

Tomorrow would be another day.

For a complete list of those left alive in Manhattan City after this fateful day was over, see pp. 1–1835 inclusive. *From the author's collection*